SOUND*Shifting*®

Your Personal Guide to Self-Healing with Sound

Tryshe Dhevney

Published by
Under Running Laughter Press
Tucson, Arizona

SOUND*Shifting*®
Published by Under Running Laughter Press
P.O. Box 64148, Tucson, Arizona 85728-4148

http://www.soundshifting.com

ISBN 978-0-9797159-1-4

Printed in the United States of America by Lightning Source

Design and Layout by Mikaela Quinn

Back cover photgraph by Fotovitamina

First published in the United States of America
by Under Running Laughter Press, 2010

1 3 5 7 9 10 8 6 4 2

DEDICATION

To Tim, my One Love.
Before I knew you, I knew your voice.
And then you sang me to you.

INVOCATION

Dear Reader,

In your honor, I hold this one encompassing truth . . .
that you are HAPPY;
The kind of happy that allows you
to be fully present in each moment of your life
and freely celebrate your Self.
The kind of happy where those you meet, however casually,
feel your joy,
bless you, and are blessed by you;
The kind of happy where you lead fearlessly with an open heart
and step consciously and deliberately into the unknown and flow;
The kind where your voice rings with the healing power of laughter
and shouts the irrepressible delight of being you.

You feel something shift within;
You may not know what, why, or how,
but you know you are ready for change.
You are willing to risk everything . . .
EVERY THING
. . . to have it all.
You will master YOUR VOICE as limitless potential.

There is great urgency at this time in the world.
And you, dear reader, are being called
and are guided by your heart.
You, yes, all of you, are rooted in a state of grace.

Open your voice and let out the light!

In sweet harmony,
Tryshe Dhevney
Tucson, Arizona
February 1, 2010

ACKNOWLEDGMENTS

I extend profound gratitude to my husband, Tim Flood, for his love, patience, unfailing support, inspiration and outright brilliance, without which this book would not have been possible.

To the wild-women, sisters and friends, Amayea Maat, Joan Steuer, Jeanne Kresser and Cynthia Cross for reading drafts of this manuscript and offering incredible insight, unwavering encouragement and vision beyond my own horizons.

To Billie McKibben, Pinau Merlin, Jill Ruttenberg, Deborah Mayaan, Susan Cooper, Geraldine Jaffe, all sisters-who-write, who, during the early phase of this manuscript, left indelible fingerprints.

To Athena and Bill Steen for the use of their casita so that I could spread my ideas out upon the desert floor and dream out loud.

To Mikaela Quinn for her care and skill in birthing this book.

I thank them all, my students and clients for the teachings they offered me during our time together.

To my family, whose continued support lifts my spirit and feeds my soul.

A special thanks to my grandchildren, Gabriella and Trevor, who always live their lives out loud and remind me of the bounty of the Universe.

Finally, with deep affection and appreciation to Mom and Dad, who I believe, were they still alive, would be pleased that I kept my promise to write this book.

TABLE OF CONTENTS

"I have not come to teach what you know not;
I have come to deepen in you that wisdom which is yours already."

—Hazrat Inayat Khan, Sufi Master

Preface

What if one sound, one simple focused sound that any of us can make, could alter the trajectory of a moment or the molecular structure of a cell? Seem far-fetched? Imagining such ideas allowed me to enter a world of sound alchemy, where one's voice can create tones that fill the soul and touch the edges of the Universe.

In the years since my recovery from hepatitis C and liver disease, I have created SOUND*Shifting*®. Through my lectures, workshops, and consultations, I've seen people transform their lives—dissolve chronic anxiety, eliminate respiratory diseases, discover sexual health, and much more. I've become a passionate facilitator in assisting others to find their voice and generate healing tones to allow optimum health. All who open their minds and consciously choose to engage sound as a healing and balancing modality experience dramatic results. These shifts happen quickly for some and take more time with others. In short, through the sounds of our voices, we can actively expand consciousness while being fully awake and present in the moment. As I see it, this is the heart of bliss.

We're all endowed with the means to heal ourselves physically, mentally, spiritually, and financially. How?

If you're like me, you don't want to wade through page after page searching for answers. You want to know this: How can I feel good NOW? How can I experience wholeness, even enlightenment, at the grocery store, at work, while filling the car with gas, driving the kids to soccer practice?

There's no need to migrate to a mountaintop. Wholeness is in this moment. Right here, right now, fingering the pages of this book. My intent is that every chapter leads you to your own

Lifetime after lifetime our soul identity is awakened through sound .... once heard, the Sound calls our soul into the proper dimension and we begin to vibrate at the rate of our Soul Frequency...

Ancient Zen Teaching

sound value. Your voice holds the key to real power in your life. It would be my great honor to be your personal soundshifter, cheering you on as you chart your healing course, whatever your symptoms or state of being.

Let the practical tools of the Chakra Tones offered here help you begin the process of changing long-held beliefs and expectations that influence every aspect of your life. Soon you will begin to understand the power of choice, both conscious and unconscious. You will see that accepting full responsibility for every little thing in your life is what opens the floodgates of joy and power. The sound of your own voice and the messages from your body will align with what you truly love. You will know because you will see it in your life.

A resonant, radiant voice is awakening within. It will be heard, for it carries vibrational perfection—your soul. You hold a constant longing, a desire to experience the sound of your true Self as whole, passionate, vibrant, and masterful. Silence this voice and you deny who you are at the very core of your being. Express the unexpressed joys and sorrows and all that's been hidden away out of shame, guilt, or the effort to survive and you'll discover a new friend and ally. You're invited to feel, to laugh with abandon from the depths of your being.

Remember, all is within your reach and only a tone away—your tone.

1

Cracks in the Wall

My Story

Arrival 1996

Having U-Hauled to the southwestern desert during a seismic shift in my life, solid ground seemed wrenched from under me. Rapidly approaching middle age, I was newly married and had no local friends or family, and no job. I found myself living in an unfurnished house with my husband and two cats who were too afraid to leave their travel cage.

All around me coyotes haunted the edges of the canyon, puncturing the night stillness with their yelps. Scorpions crept in the dark corners of my closet. Coiled snakes and Gila monsters threatened my morning walks while the sun blazed in the dry desert sky. The earth cracked beneath me and I straddled two worlds—the one I left behind and the one I had barely entered. It seemed I was at the mercy of powerful desert forces that were suddenly stripping away all the extraneous "stuff" that, up to this point, had defined my life. No time to settle in and find my rhythm; the time had come to cut to my essence.

Diagnosis 1998

A routine medical check-up with my new health care provider showed I had hepatitis C compounded by cirrhosis of the liver. The medical establishment was vague as to what to do about this new strain of hepatitis. In fact, the doctors seemed quite confounded. If I wanted answers, it would be up to me to dig deeper.

I began devouring every piece of literature about hepatitis C I could put my hands on. Still not satisfied, I trolled the Internet for solutions to ease my growing fears. *Well, that was a mistake!* I learned never to rely on the web as the final word; it

And the day came when the risk it took to remain tightly closed in a bud was more painful than the risk it took to bloom.

Anaïs Nin

can be depressing. So can the doctors. As a product of the late '60s counterculture, I was convinced Western medicine would more likely kill me than heal me. From the perspective of Western medicine, it appeared I could look forward to two possible futures: a) dying quickly or b) dying in a month.

Ironically, I'd begun teaching sound as an alternative healing modality at Miraval Life In Balance, a health resort and spa in Tucson. Daily, I instructed others to use their own voice to create sound health. Consumed by a need to help my clients, I placed their needs, their concerns, their health before mine. What a well-intentioned setup for a painful awakening! Gradually, I began to understand that my singular focus on service to others might actually be making me sick.

Taking a step back, I could see times when the world was less than appreciative of my overtures to "help." And if I was not meddling, fixing, changing, or controlling enough, I was fostering a kind of dependence from others on my time and energy. That growing sucking sound that was following me around was the sound of the life force being *hoovered* right out of me.

Still, I blindly served. These unintended interventions forced me to see that my good works would serve no one unless and until I was in service to myself first. I had to take my attention off everyone else and make me and my health the priority.

A life-threatening disease will definitely focus one's attention like a laser beam. Bottom line, I very much wanted to live. I quickly focused on any and all possible alternative methods to heal what I came to understand as the "killer" virus; a virus with no known cure. I tried laying on of hands, psychic surgery, acupuncture, meditation, Chinese herbs, changing my diet, not changing my diet—you name it. I even made a desperate attempt to reach country singer Naomi Judd, who'd been diagnosed with hepatitis C in 1991. Surely she would know what to do.

Back then, Naomi was not talking. And though I sleuthed through every paragraph of her book, *Love Can Build A Bridge*, nothing about a cure could be found. It was rumored that she was seeking some form of alternative therapy, but the public story was different. In print, she was treated successfully with Interferon and only that. However, today, with the growing acceptance of integrative medicine, Naomi has become a tireless advocate for combining alternative and conventional medicine. We've come a long way since the '90s.

Still, the healing gift of sound eluded me. So simple, so accessible, so powerful, and so obvious was this gift that I didn't hear it coming from my own mouth.

It's Your Life!

Out of the blue, a friend of a friend called. Her bizarre voice and words literally altered my DNA and changed the course of my life. *"For crying out loud!"* she shouted at me through the phone. *"This is YOUR body! You decide! Not the doctors, not your best friend, not even your husband!"* I held the receiver away from me. Who is this woman? Normally I would have hung up. But something compelled me to keep listening. And though she was yelling at me, it felt like her voice was from another dimension, another paradigm I wasn't familiar with . . . at least not yet. *"You can CHOOSE how this will turn out. It's your body. IT'S YOUR LIFE!"* The force of her words pried open the door to possibility and kicked me right through it.

It became increasingly clear to me that my first team of doctors was at a loss as to how to eradicate this viral menace. Their uninspiring monotones spoken in bile green treatment rooms with faded brown linoleum floors only amplified my concerns.

In May 2000, when my viral load (the amount of virus mutating in my system) spiked to an extremely high level, I received a breath-stopping message . . . on my answering machine! The lead doctor droned, *"We've run out of treatment options and suggest you get your affairs in order. We're terribly sorry but there's nothing we can do for you now."*

Wait a minute! He must be reading the wrong chart! He can't be talking about me! I went searching for another doctor and within 24 hours I was sitting in the waiting room of my new M.D.

This new, and yes, much improved doctor suggested immediate treatment with Interferon (a synthetic reproduction of the Interferon naturally produced in our bodies). Injecting this chemical "cocktail" to fight viruses by boosting the immune system was the most hopeful approach of the day. Dog-tired and increasingly disconnected from life among the living, I finally surrendered. As I sat there listening to the doctor describe the medical realities facing me, a sweetly strange sensation crept over me. My jaw softened, my shoulders released, and for that moment, I found the place between desire and fear. Then it hit me. I was letting go.

I stopped projecting a cure for my future and became still. All my fears about how to handle chemo and the damage I believed their medicine might inflict became nonexistent. My resistance—to the treatment, to Western medicine, to doctors, to my anger, even to resistance yet unnamed but ever present up to this point—simply vaporized. In hindsight, this moment was the quintessence of my journey to whole-body health. I had experienced a state of true freedom, without which healing cannot begin.

July 2000 marked the time I willingly stepped into the AMA approach and let my doctor take a serious crack at my "condition."

July 7, 2000
Journal Entry

Okay, I did it. Shot myself for the first time. Squeezing a tiny bubble of Interferon from the pen-styled syringe to clear potential air bubbles, something surfaced from the depths of my body/brain . . . a cellular memory. I had to laugh.

Flashback to San Francisco, 1968—a slum walk-up in North Beach. Sitting on a dank, faux Persian carpet in dim light, my upper right arm is "tied off" . . . a belt, maybe, or a scarf. Veins defined by an elaborate blue highway run down my arm. They throb. He says I have good veins. It feels comforting there's something good about me. I guess I'm glad. The band Cream blasts out of the stereo "I feel free . . . ." He slaps my arm. My skin yields as he sinks the needle deep into one of those "good" veins. He loosens the belt. Speed screams through my bloodstream. My brain explodes . . . a simultaneous surge both out of body and sucker-punched into my body. I fall back onto the floor. White-out.

I had to have someone else shoot the speed into my vein for a few convenient reasons: a) I didn't know how; b) I was scared; and c) if someone else did it, I could build the case that I was not an addict. My argument was based on the "Reefer Madness" drug culture perception that addicts inject themselves. Everyone knows that!

So here I am today at an ironic crossroad, having to inject myself with the prescribed "cure" for a disease I contracted most likely when I injected speed into my arm (one of three times) 43 years ago. Strange, how the circles and cycles of my life intersect.

My husband, Tim, was sweet. He stood at my back, gently massaging the knots in my neck. As we breathed together, his hand squeezing encouragement into my shoulder, we offered up personal prayers. We agreed that fear of this disease was a more insidious killer than the hepatitis C. We didn't want the presence of fear anywhere near us. In fact, we agreed to keep this whole Interferon thing a secret.

Thoughts are as powerful as words and travel in microseconds through a vibrational network that's universal, so I don't want people to project their fears (although well-meaning) onto me. We've told his close friend and one of my girlfriends, my son, a co-worker, and my boss. They've all been instructed to hold only positive thoughts when they think of me or us during this time. No pity, no worry, no fear. Please!

The pharmacy nurse gave us an over-the-counter litany of what to expect as possible side effects of this treatment—hair loss, low energy, loss of appetite—but even with these, I realize I have a choice. I choose to hold the thought that the side effects will be minimal if they exist at all! I found myself making this little statement out loud as I emptied the syringe into my thigh. "As I inject this chemical into my leg, each cell in my body knows to use what it wants for healing, and what my body doesn't want is eliminated immediately." This brought me peace. I'll say it every time.

How different was this soft, quivering space of a hopeful heart from the hardness of that jagged story of long ago.

Discovering Sound
2000

With my "treatment" barely underway, I knew I was in uncharted medical territory. To comfort myself, I turned to my Tibetan singing bowl. I'd fallen in love with this amazing instrument at the Gem and Mineral Show in Tucson. Its intoxicating beauty reeled me back to a time years ago, when I had been initiated into the Sufi Order and joined the Boston-based Om Theatre acting company. Sufism speaks to my heart, then and now. It celebrates the ancient mysteries of sound and its role in transforming our lives. As a spiritually hungry 20-something, I had been entranced by the mystical tones, the dancing, the limitless possibilities presenting themselves. Daily, we would experiment with the impact of sound, movement, and music on the deeper landscape of the body and mind. One of the meditative techniques we used was a timed period of sustained single-toned chanting, after which we would monitor our body's responses. Little did I know that these very same tones would one day save my life. These tones are the foundation of the healing sound I offer you in this book.

During the time when I could do little more than sprawl on the sofa, I had enough strength to do one thing—play my singing bowl. Each time I glided the striker around the bowl's rim, the tones coaxed from me songs beyond words—sweet, unfamiliar tones that kept my soul from splintering into a million pieces. A subtle strength began replacing my fear.

I did not fully get it then, but sound was saving my life.

As I continued to tone, I began to observe the relationship between my thoughts, words, and physical body. Concepts I'd explored in my long-ago past started resurfacing. Stacked next to my bed were titles like *The Mysticism of Sound* by Hazrat Inayat Khan, *The Only Diet There IS* by Saundra Ray, and Shakti Gawain's book *Creative Visualization*, all old friends offering new and urgent meaning for me.

Simply put, they all agreed: we live in a boundless Universe, one made up entirely of vibration. Our Universe and everything in it—humans, trees, animals, birds, songs, words, thoughts, and feelings—are pure energy. Cars, computers, chairs, DVDs, and shopping carts are also pure energy, even our postal carriers . . . pure vibration. And everything that vibrates creates sound. Even the organs of our bodies "sing" their own melodies that are fundamental to their natural healthy state. Yes, we are living, breathing, and walking symphonies of sound vibrations.

The thoughts we think, the words we speak, and the physical sensations and emotions we feel broadcast a frequency into the world the way a radio broadcasts radio waves. The quality of that frequency creates the physical, emotional, and spiritual reality we live in.

Clearly we don't have to know the physics to understand such axioms as *like attracts like; as within, so without*; and *as above, so below*. Convert that into day-to-day experiences and we see that what we put out is what comes back. Nothing can come to us unless it finds something in us with which it is attuned. If we worry, we will attract more things to worry about, and more worriers to worry right along with us.

If we are feeling peaceful or relaxed, the Law of Attraction reminds us that as energy, we will line up with circumstances and people that match that same easy-feeling frequency.

Whether positive or negative, our thoughts will show up in our lives. If we can't "stomach" certain events or people, we may have just discovered the reason our stomach hurts from time to time.

I began to see that everything I thought or said out loud mattered. In fact, what mattered most became matter. What I hadn't taken into account was the impact sound was having on my body, my brain, and my state of being.

Gradually these flashes of insight gave way to understanding. I could see that everything is vibrating at some level of motion and every molecule of my being acts with a magnetic pull, drawing to me experiences that correlate with my vibration. Aha! The dots were lining up.

Nourished by these reminders and several weeks of toning, I began to step back from emotions that used to shroud me in despair. Okay, I may not be able to run a marathon and my hair is falling out from the injections. Sure, I feel weak and I'm on the sofa AND it's a beautiful day. *All is well.*

Recognizing I had the power to redirect my thoughts and create feelings that made me stronger was my first conscious shift.

Healing and curing are not synonymous. Cure refers to complete biological resolution of a disease state, while healing refers to a revitalizing and regenerative process that can occur on emotional, spiritual or physical levels—and sometimes on all three levels at once.

Michael Lerner, Ph.D.
Commonweal Cancer Help Program, Bolinas, CA.
(San Francisco Conference 2006)
www.commonweal.org

November 9, 2000
Journal Entry

My doctor is growing concerned that my white blood count is dipping dangerously low. He's always seemed so confident that the Interferon will wipe out this virus, but I heard something else in his voice during today's visit. I don't want to say "hopeless," but I could tell he had that worst-case scenario realization in his head. With each weekly visit, he monitors and modifies. I too am a little uneasy. This was to be a yearlong protocol and it's only been three months. So, if my body rejects the chemical, even after he adjusts the dosage from three times a week to twice a week and I take just two pills . . . try injecting only once and forget the pills . . . (cross your fingers) . . . now try taking just the pills . . . .

I have to believe something else is afoot. Time to trust the body on this one.

In truth, I think my cells are communicating directly to both the doc and me—but I'm the only one who can hear them. I believe the thought frequencies I hold each time I inject are received by my body/brain—a kind of a direct download into my cells. My inner sense tells me I'm getting well. Seems like my body is signaling us both to stop this chemical invasion by dropping the white blood count. Whoa . . . incredible how this works! The doc can't justify keeping me on this Interferon/Ribaviron stuff much longer. In his paradigm, it was a long shot at best, but something else is going on here. I feel it.

I don't mind losing 12 pounds. That's a good thing. But the next time I want to drop some weight, maybe I could just eat more greens and forget the chemo. I love options!

I was not dying as the doctor feared. I was healing. And as I have since discovered, there is far more to healing than curing.

November 23, 2000
Journal Entry

The strangest thing happened today. As I curled up on the sofa (something I do for hours these days), I posed a question to the ethers. Okay, Universe, why did I get this disease, anyway, aside from the obvious needle use of a lifetime ago? Where did it come from? Why this disease when I could have had any other or none? What's happening here? And better yet, what am I supposed to learn? I hardly finished the question when a strong, clear thought crossed my mind. *It's an easy way to say NO!*

As I took in this bizarre idea, I found myself squinting for clarity as if my brain could read the fine print in the ethers. The answer came quickly and clearly. I had contracted hepatitis C and chronic liver disease to help me set boundaries, in essence, to say *no*.

Here I was, having an open conversation with god-knows-what, yet every cell in my body shimmied. I get it! I have to tell the truth, set some boundaries, maybe even let go of my work with the kids . . . all of it—them, their alcoholism, their parents, the touring. Yet, I get so seduced by the "good work," the accolades and personal strokes, not to mention the genuine pride I have for what those young people have accomplished. For nearly 20 years I have carried this vision. I know what we have is special and unique. As a peer-to-peer theatre of prevention, we have provided a powerful message of recovery to audiences across this country.

For too long young people have been the forgotten population in today's "war on drugs." And because of this work—this living, breathing, feeling stage—we have made a difference. So how can I let this go when it is changing so many lives? Who will take up the mantle and carry on with the work? Will it, should it, carry on?

But I really do want to let it go . . . move on and explore, if for no other reason than to have a LIFE beyond addiction. But then what? Who am I without this work? Who will I become? Will I stay sober? Will I find myself on some *Where are they now* website page? I'll be letting everyone down—the kids, the mission, the world! Okay, maybe that's a little grandiose, but it's my life right now! I never felt my own recovery in jeopardy and figured I would weather this storm, again, if I maintain my focus, my priority.

Once I took a couple of breaths and settled down, I let the answer waft through me again. Well, if that's all I have to do, I can easily say no out loud and directly from now on. No—to the work, the people, to whatever and whomever—out loud.

In that moment, I shuddered as if an entity had been exorcised from my being. Shaking it off, I laid back into the knowing. I am living in well-being. I took a nap.

No Trace of Virus
December 2000

Sure enough, a week after my doctor stopped the chemical invasion, he drew more blood to confirm his concern. Instead, he was surprised, actually stunned, by disbelief. *There was no trace of the virus.* He managed to say he was guardedly optimistic, not believing his own eyes and the test results in his hand.

For two years in my aftercare visits, he continued to be mystified yet sincerely glad that I was no longer sick. However, I could see his brain trying to reformat the path of my recovery to make it fit into his medical paradigm. He called me his Miracle Girl.

Yet, this was no miracle. Instead, it was evidence of an evolving shift in consciousness. I was waking up to the truth of my own vibrational perfection. Now, to be honest, I would not have phrased it that way back then, but this is what was occurring: my physical body was offering direct, stunning evidence of whole-body health, or *resonance* as I call it today. I was consciously creating my physical reality. The first indication came when I knew, through every cell of my body, that I had the power to redirect my thoughts and thus heal my body. The second indication came as a confirmation.

After one of my bi-annual checkups, my doctor's nurse took me aside and almost as an afterthought, said, "There's something else going on here that you need to understand. The reason he's completely confused by your case," she continued, "is because your genotype is not the type that would respond to Interferon." Taken aback, I pressed for more clarity. "You mean, there's no medical reason for me to be well?" She nodded.

Her words brought everything into focus, launching another round of Ahas! in a life that would continue to be filled with joyful Ahas! Indeed there was something bigger going on here. I became a detective, hungrily retracing my early and current experiences with sound and intention, with the letting go of resistance, with the opening of my mind/body/spirit to the frequency of "All Is Well."

Years have passed since my doctor declared me "cured" of hepatitis C and liver disease, and the alchemy of sound continues to reveal its mysteries and magic. Layer by layer, these sound currents offer keys to tangible bliss. The power inherent in the voice to elevate vibration, heal and balance the body/brain, and open the unlimited potential encoded in each cell rests at the tip of the tongue.

If your life is dominated by a health crisis, or you long for calm at the center of emotional turbulence or stand at one of many crossroads in your delicious life, I honor your creation. It is the contrast you have been waiting for, one that will cast your net upon the sea of possibility. You are eager to set the course for this journey, knowing it is an adventure in magic and wonder.

There is no mistake or failure, not regret or turning back. You are making the only choice that feels right—to elevate your vibration and accept the knowledge, awareness, and holographic wisdom that is innately yours.

I am excited and honored to take this sound journey with you now. We will begin where you are.

JUST THE FACTS

I'm neither a scientist nor a researcher. However, given the dramatic shift in my health, I was hungry to know more. To start, I began reviewing the facts I already knew, a kind of connect-the-dots line drawing. What did science have to say, if anything, about my "miracle?" I combed the Internet, medical research papers, and spiritual books embracing anything and everything that might codify what had happened to my body and mind.

Sometime in my early days of meditation, a passing comment from a yoga instructor had elbowed its way into my consciousness and had remained there. The thought was simple: *sound energizes the breath.* Another dot was connected when I read somewhere in a medical journal the phrase *a virus cannot exist in an oxygen-rich environment.* BANG! It hit me. My toning might, in fact, be oxygenating my blood and lymph systems, strengthening my immune system. This, in turn, might be allowing my body to do what it does naturally—activate the vitality of each cell thereby allowing my body to BE WELL. This seemed bigger than me.

From earliest recorded history, we know that many ancient cultures had a sophisticated understanding of the relationship of sound and human consciousness. Though they may have lacked any way to scientifically measure their experience, the fact remains that sound was integral to these ancient people. Our ancestors embraced sound as the very essence of life itself. They understood what modern science is now beginning to discover, that we live in a sea of vibration—the source of all form, the source of all thought. From drumming to chanting, they lived what we now understand, that the human body/brain is transformed on a molecular level by the frequencies of sound and rhythm.

Sound enters the healing equation from several directions: It may alter cellular functions through energetic effects; it may calm the mind and therefore the body, or it may have emotional effects, which influence neurotransmitters and neuropeptides, which in turn help to regulate the immune system—the healer within.

Mitchell Gaynor, M.D.
Founder, President of Gaynor Integrative Oncology,
Consultant and former Director of Medical Oncology at The Strang Cancer Prevention Center
Author of *The Healing Power of Sound: Recovery from Life-Threatening Illness Using Sound, Voice, and Music*

Sound As Ancient Medicine

Pythagoras, the mathematician, mystic, and scientist, was considered by some to be the Godfather of Modern Sound

Medicine. He taught his students to use sound and music to soothe the spirit, release worry, fear, and anger and enhance joy and happiness. He explained how sound functions in relation to the universe: ". . . Each and every atom produces a particular sound on account of its movement, its rhythm or vibration. All these sounds and vibrations form a universal harmony in which each element, while having its own function and character, contribute to the whole."

Our own bodies are microcosms of that celestial symphony. Using sound to heal and achieve balance from within has been practiced for thousands of years in India, Asia, Africa, and Europe, and among the Aboriginal and Native American peoples.

The Tibetans still use bells, chimes, bowls, and chanting as the foundation of their spiritual practice. And in Bali, Indonesia, the echoing gamelan, gong, and drum are used in ceremonies to enchant people.

Since the human body is over seventy percent water and since sound travels five times more efficiently through water than through air, sound frequency stimulation directly into the body is a highly efficient means for total body stimulation, especially at the cellular level. Direct stimulation of living cellular tissue using sound frequency vibration has shown marked cellular metabolism and therefore a possible mobilization of a cellular healing response.

Jeffrey Thompson, D.C. B.F.A., Director of the Center for Neuroacoustic Research; "Sound—Medicine for the New Millennium" www.neuroacoustic.com/nemill.html; 1/23/2010

Among the Australian Aboriginals and Native American shamans, vocal toning and repetitive sound vibration with instruments of nature are used in sacred ceremony to adjust imbalances of the spiritual, emotional, or physical being. Even further back in time, we find the priests of ancient Egypt knew how to use vowel sounds to resonate their energy centers or chakras. A direct link exists between different parts of the body and specific sounds.

Science tells us that all that exists in the universe is present in human form, that our bodies are pure vibration, an energetic reality of sound, light, and matter. The universe is the macrocosm; the body the microcosm.

Exploring how science incorporates sound helped me understand that the goal is to restore resonant frequencies in the body. My intuition provided many of the theories I posit in this book. The less occupied I was with intellectually "finding" the answers, the more sound opened up my pathway of knowledge and understanding.

Mitchell Gaynor's statement about the healing power of sound pulled it all together for me. I understood that my own voice is a powerful tool, and when allowed to express without resistance, it becomes a powerful delivery system for life-giving energy. His statement helped me understand the roll of sound in my personal healing.

Sound functioned as a sledgehammer breaking up old resistive patterns, rapidly bringing me to a more balanced state of body and mind. My attitude shifted—most notably, my focus changed from dying to the reality of ease.

Wired For Sound

Late in 2003, I was offered an opportunity to participate in a brain-mapping experiment with biofeedback. Biofeedback is a widely used and medically accepted technique for measuring heart rate and other body functions while teaching us how to relax and reduce stress. It makes you aware of any unconscious "involuntary" physical reactions you may have to stress – "feeding back" subtle changes in your stress levels.

This experiment, conducted by a Ph.D., was not part of any controlled research project for peer-review or publication, but more for our own edification. Besides, the cost to fund such research these days is out of this world, so I was happy to "experiment" with outcomes and satisfied by the biofeedback results.

Wired to the monitoring device, I began vocalizing each of the Chakra Tones (see Chapter 6), the primordial tones I had used for healing my hepatitis C virus (HCV) and liver disease. With each tone he measured the impact of the frequencies on my brain. The needle would dance, feeding data from my voice, to the brain, through my skin and finally, to the device. To the trained professional, each code, each type of movement means something. When we were done, he summarized what he saw.

After toning the entire range of Chakra Tones the outcome was notable: the vocal tones had produced what he had described as a combined Alpha/Theta brain wave state. The brain wave frequencies produced by the tones were equal to what is produced by a 30-minute meditation session—extremely effective in reducing stress and highly advantageous for self-healing. Another exciting discovery was that these frequencies produced a brain state that allowed me to be more suggestible to an affirmation or new thought. Even though I can always feel the energy of sound move through various parts of my body, it was especially fascinating and gratifying to have science corroborate my experience.

I was heartened to find that so many in the traditional medical field are serious about sound research and its impact on the body/mind. Current medical models for providing health in our country are being challenged to include in their overall philosophy a vision for wellness. Those of us in the holistic/alternative

In Alpha [brain state], unlike Theta and Delta, a person is aware of his or her body. . . . The body is relaxed, which is why Alpha training is so effective in stress management. By training a person to produce Alpha at will, s/he is able to greatly reduce the stresses in his or her life. It is neurophysiologically difficult for most people to experience states of agitation or stress in Alpha or Theta. . . . Theta [brain state] is the ideal state for some types of accelerated learning, self-programming and psycho-immunology (self-healing). . . .

Tom Kenyon, M.A.
Brain States
Lithia Springs, GA: New Leaf Publishing, 2001, p. 39.

field of healing are seeing what we've known and practiced intuitively now supported by science.

There is an out-of-the-box mind set among young doctors and research scientists that approach medicine from a different paradigm. This next wave of new thinkers in medicine further bolsters my understanding and supports the roll that imagination plays in the future of science. Whatever part of me doubted or required proof is now quiet, at peace knowing that what I regarded as "magic" is more real than imagined.

The human voice and our conscious use of it as an instrument can penetrate and heal even the deepest shadows of our human condition.

Julia Cameron
Author of *The Artist's Way* and *Vein of Gold*

Today we have come full circle. My work with sound expands on the idea that sound is the medicine of the future. How fortunate that we are living in the "future" time when the sound of our own voices can create internal and external harmony one sound, one breath at a time.

If we could receive, in real time, the visual scope and movement of vibration created by our physical bodies, thoughts, emotions and words, we would be overwhelmed by the elegant complexities and flow of who we truly are as vibration.

To live in attunement is to stand in the midst of your dreams knowing that you are the reason for this limitless Universal bounty. Sound is the most direct pathway to being happier than you've ever been, laughing harder, smiling wider, standing taller, walking lighter, dancing crazier, hugging longer, living grander, loving louder—being, in essence, your Super Natural Self.

This one thing, I know.

Life Is But A Dream

Ever notice there are times you'd rather get a root canal than open your mouth and make sound? The embarrassment can be paralyzing. Believe me, I know.

At nine years old, in the first of many recurring torments during reading time, I'd sit as still as a deer caught in headlights, petrified that Sister St. Whoever would call on me to read out loud. I'd hold my breath and pray to spontaneously combust. Surely, the whole class could hear my heart jack-hammering in my chest.

When she inevitably did call my name, I stood, reluctantly, swallowed air and opened my mouth. Nothing but a strained gagging noise ever escaped from it. On the off chance there really was Someone listening, I let loose the silent prayer, *Please God, let my eyes tell my brain that my mouth needs to speak, or I will have to die.*

I'd cough and start again—the same gagging squeak. Kids snickered. Afraid to exhale, I swallowed more air, stumbling and pitching through a paragraph whose end was several million words away. With each breath, each word, my voice grew tighter and higher, the laughter louder.

My face flashed a bright Irish pink and I prayed again—this time to the Saint of Hopeless Readers—to make the paragraph end. Eventually, it did.

In utter humiliation, I slumped in my chair. *I can never speak in class again. I CAN NEVER SHOW MY FACE IN SCHOOL AGAIN.*

Noise:
1) a sound, esp. a loud or unpleasant or undesired one,
2) a confused sound of voices and movements,
3) outcry, disturbance.

The Concise OXFORD Dictionary

Shhhhhhh . . .

As young children, we naturally and freely enjoy making noise, dancing wildly, joyously being distracted by a bug, inspired by a feather, and letting our imaginations run amuck. So what happens to that inherent sense of wonder and spontaneity? It becomes swallowed up by the family's agenda. Our little human "I AM" seeds take root in a soil that's absorbed the restrictive beliefs and limiting expectations passed down through generations. You may have endured days, months, and years of messages such as these: *It's just the way we have always been. Children should be seen and not heard! If you can't say anything nice, don't say anything at all,* or *How could you be so stupid?*

Is it any wonder we shut down? We learn that if we're good girls and boys who tell the truth others want to hear, we will be rewarded. These stories are told over and over again. Sadly, we end up telling the stories ourselves to our own children.

What about you and your young voice? Take a moment to recall any experiences in which you censored or completely swallowed your voice. Were you:

- Scolded for being outspoken?
- Intimidated? "If I hear another word out of you, I'll . . ."
- Told to "Watch your mouth, young lady!"?
- Asked to stop singing and "just mouth the words"?
- Warned that crying or showing your feelings would land you in trouble?
- Scoffed at? "Suck it up!"
- Told "When I want your opinion I'll ask for it!"?
- Or mocked for the way you spoke or how you sounded?

This list presents a sampling of the vocal seeds and distortions I've heard from clients over the years. These silencing memories are all distorted perceptions that form the basis for who we believe we are. Such experiences don't leave us simply because we age. Though I'm no longer triggered by the memory of my reading trauma, I can vividly conjure up every scintilla of shame, even decades later.

A Noisy Way Of Life

What is noise? And what relationship does it have to sound?

More than a disturbance, noise is the sound of resistance. From a wellness perspective, noise is the lifelong accumulation of misperception. The meaningless drivel clamoring inside our heads delivers a litany of "less-thans."

Given that we were very little when these words began defining our self-perception, we accepted them as truth. We believed that the lie told over and over again was real.

This kind of noise builds walls and keeps consciousness fixed in place. Because we've lived stuck for so long, we don't recognize that unconditional love could ever exist for us, that financial abundance is our heritage, that physical, emotional, mental, and moral well-being is our enlightened design.

Conversely, we think miracles are anomalies, *don't kid yourself, life is hard . . . success happens for those who do more and work hardest (no pain, no gain) . . . look out for the other shoe to drop.* What's happening? Instead of accepting our Master Self, we're rejecting it. We put another brick in our wall of denial and succumb to the noisy habit of distraction and personal distortion.

Curiously, the origin of the word noise comes from the Latin, nausea, meaning to make sick. This connected a few important dots for me. We mindlessly language these disturbing inner "voices" of misperception with words like I can't, I'll try, I have to, I don't know, I'd like to but, I should, I want, I wish I could, if only, maybe. Once these verbal saboteurs are given voice, they trigger electrical charges in the brain informing the entire system to respond according to our perceptions, our beliefs.

Neuroscientist Candace Pert, Ph.D., in her book *Molecules of Emotion*, explains that "neuropeptides—the chemicals triggered by emotions—are thoughts converted into matter. . . Emotions reside physically in our bodies and interact with our cells and tissues. . . . Often the body responds emotionally and manufactures emotional chemicals even before the brain has registered a problem." (pp. 133-134)

In fact, our brains are mapping the data of our lives, giving meaning or value to every experience and storing it as cellular memory. So when we speak from the "noise"—build a case around it, meditate on it, live by it, and defend it—we eventually become sick. Our bodies are doing exactly what we tell them to do!

Empty is a sensation, not an idea . . . a feeling, not a concept. As a sensation, even the word empty short-circuits the active mind. It is itself a destination, one with no past and no future. The art of EMPTY begins with your focus on the jaw as you let it fall open.

Tryshe Dhevney

The How Of "Now"

Enough about the issues! How do we shift?

For a moment, just sit. Listen to sounds outside of you—the sound of air moving around the room or the wind outside, a radio playing in the distance, maybe the chimes in the yard lightly tickled by a breeze, a car ignition turning over, a bird announcing itself to the waiting day, water dripping from the faucet. Notice this: Can you capture the textures and tones that make up this moment?

At first glance, you think you are alone. Everything appears empty and silent. But given a deeper listen, sounds appear in layers—tones, colors, overtones, some you can easily identify while others draw their shape from a sensation. Part of that soundscape is your own breath . . . ah, sweet mystery. Follow your breath all the way out. Empty . . . completely empty. Don't worry; you will breathe again when your body is ready. Keep observing the cycle of your breath and don't judge. No matter how the breath changes, deep or shallow, just continue to follow it . . . in and all the way out.

Now allow yourself to experience your breath breathing you.

EXERCISE: Being Breathed

1. Sit comfortably.
2. Gently lift your chest and spine upward, and soften your abdominal muscles. And begin to watch your breath.
3. Notice how continuous your breathing is, effortless, no beginning and no end. But we tend to think of one breath as beginning with an inhalation and ending with exhalation. See if you can reverse this perception in this exercise.
4. Focus your attention on the breath and let it come of its own accord without trying to change it.
5. Now, experience exhalation as the beginning of each new cycle. The reason for doing this is that you have more control over exhalation, because you can use the voluntary muscles between your ribs to squeeze air out of your lung. This muscle movement is more powerful than what you use for drawing air in.
6. Breathe with this conscious awareness as often as is comfortable.

Are you feeling brave? Want to try a little sound?

7. When you exhale, let out a loud sigh; at the end of the sigh push the rest of the breath out of the belly. Notice how deep and resonant that sound is. Repeat a couple of times.
8. Now ease into the vocals and give voice to the vowel tones – aa (as in play), ee (as in glee), ah (as in awe), oh (as in so), and ooo (as in smooth) – sliding the tones higher in pitch then lower on the length of each breath. Play in this sonic sandbox as often as you think of it.

As you do the exercise, at some point pause and notice how your body feels. Are you breathing a little deeper? Maybe you feel a bit more peaceful, more relaxed? Just seconds of toning will lower your blood pressure, reduce stress, and energize the breath. This moves more oxygen through the body/brain, relaxes the muscles, and stimulates the flow of energy throughout your body. As you hold these tones, you accelerate the release of any resistance and create an experience of *being in the flow*. What have you got to lose—except maybe a little suffocating fear or the stress of a vein-popping day? Not only will you feel better but the world around you will reflect your good feeling as well.

To release or let go really means to not engage. It is an activity of consciously choosing non-action. Now, many of us think we are released because we can *intellectualize* the concept of relaxing; but lurking in the subterranean world of form is a body tied in knots, or NOTS (***not*** very good at that, ***not*** enough money, ***not*** capable, ***not*** free to speak, ***not*** the right weight, ***not*** young or old enough, ***not*** pretty, ***not*** smart, etc.) With all these "nots" embedded in our system, is it surprising that the jaw and tongue continue to be tied up in tension?

This tension is involuntary, meaning we are no longer conscious that it exists at all. Therefore, we believe we're not in control of the pain it's causing. As it relates to your jaw, involuntary tension is tension you can't see or feel until it manifests physically as TMJ, teeth grinding, or jaw displacement.

Another form of resistance masquerading as tension can find expression "sideways," often regrettably, such as in sarcasm, emotions erupting out of context, indirect communication. If the tongue is tense, the jaw is tense. If the jaw is tense, the neck is tense, and if the neck is tense, you can bet the breath is stuck in a never-ending loop of resistance. What emerge are patterns of holding or withholding fostered by fear. When you're in resistance, you can't hear the silent urges of what you truly love. Life is no longer vivid. Instead, life is a grind.

Sadly, and all too often, we are clouded by beliefs that nobody is home and nothing is in there or that could never happen for me. And the jaw tightens. So let it all go and untie those "nots."

Whenever you notice your neck tighten or jaw fix, pause and slightly lift your head upward, not too much, letting the jaw fall slack. Open your mouth and release an audible sighing

EXERCISE: Jaw Drop

Send your critical mind out on a break and find a comfy chair – one that will support your lower back – and just settle in. Arrange your body so you can easily sit upright with your feet comfortably placed on the floor in front of you. If sitting cross-legged works better for you, do so. Whatever your preference, be comfortable.

1. See if you can imagine your spine stacking one by one on top of the other. Those of you familiar with Yoga understand how to extend the spine. However, if this is completely new, try this. As you are seated, bring your awareness to your hips and gently tilt or roll your pelvis forward just a bit, creating a slight arch in your lower back. Let your belly roll out in front of you and soften the tummy muscles.
2. Now lift your heart (or the center of your chest) upward. Feel that wonderful extension? Even though you are upright, let it be an easy upright. As you sit and extend, be aware of no strain or tension anywhere in your body. Imagine that you are suspended and supported by space, with every muscle released, free yet connected . . . and let go.
3. Stay focused. Notice your face, skin, hair, nose, ears, lips and finally, your mouth. Go inside. Using your imagination, feel around in your mouth and let go of the muscles in your tongue, letting it fall to the floor of your mouth. Then notice your jaw and let it fall toward your chest. Can you soften the tongue a little more and allow the jaw to draw down even lower? Sigh.

Very few in this world know to what extent phenomena can be produced by the power of the voice. If there is any real trace of miracle, of phenomenon, of wonder, it is in the voice.

Hazrat Inayat Khan
Sufi Master

sound, one you might express at the end of a busy day or one that tops off a great meal, or a sigh of satisfaction after a job well done. Now that you have touched the potential of your own sound, let your voice tone a gentle Ahhhhhhhhhhhhhhh. The sound of your voice is food for the cells and music for your soul.

Release means you no longer want to force the structure of your life, and you're ready to allow life to flow in elegant synchrony.

There's no need to arrive . . . anywhere. What matters is the journey of this moment. Return to silence, like a monsoon sky, expectant and life-giving, you swell, shift, roll, and change, one cloud at a time.

December 1, 2000
Journal Entry

Finally, I have no thing to lose and nothing to do…what a game change. My fixation with *DOING* life is a fading paradigm of the past. I am ready to let go of old perceptions of what my life should look like as a woman, as a wife, as a healthy, spiritual being and in this nakedness I hear my Self, my authentic Self, my Soul. I breathe again. I am whole. This breath is holy.

From the silence I feel my heart sound. Still, it is quiet here...and very full. Silence is not the absence of sound. Silence is the absence of noise.

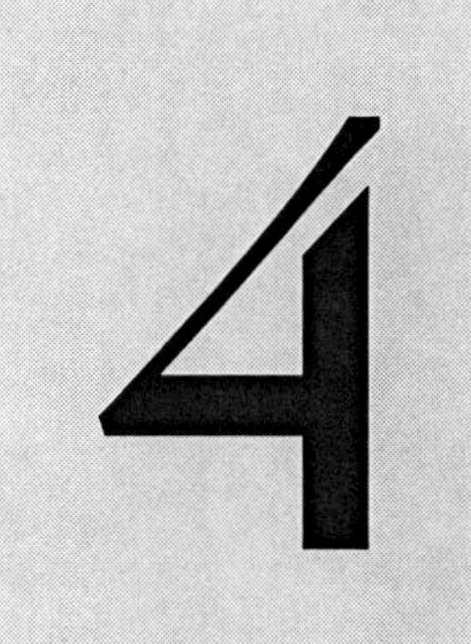

What Is The Sound Of Your Voice Saying?

The most naked part of us is our voice. Have you ever wondered who that stranger is on your voicemail claiming to be you? You may be the person who recorded the message, but there is a part of you that recognizes intuitively that that voice isn't authentic. You're right, it is a stranger. It's a voice cultivated by who you believe you are.

By editing or shutting down your voice at those critical early stages of life—to please others, to not be seen or heard, to fit in, to be appropriate—you violated something essential and sacred within. You traded being *authentic* for being *good*. The consequences are far-reaching. When we swallow our own voices, we swallow our choices, and swallowing our choices ensures that we will forfeit our personal power somewhere along our walk of life.

Be assured, you are being called on an adventure to reclaim the freedom of your childhood—real or imagined—when you sound your joyful, authentic, wildly wonderful self.

When emotions are repressed, this inhibition disarms the body's defenses against illness. Repression—dissociating emotions from awareness and relegating them to the unconscious realm—disorganizes and confuses our physiological defenses so that in some people these defenses go awry, becoming the destroyers of health rather than its protectors.

Gabor Maté M.D.
When the Body Says NO: Understanding the Stress-Disease Connection, Wiley, 2003. p. 7

Let's Hear It

Your voice is heard in a combination of ways. It reflects the quality of your breath, intention, and consciousness. Laughs, screams, groans, sighs, belches, grunts, yawns, squeals are all the sounds that accompany the movements of your life. Toning is natural . . . as natural as breathing, and it can be either conscious or unconscious.

Unconscious toning is mostly a right-brain activity, spontaneous and even intuitive. We hear it as the automatic vocal groan, sigh, hum, etc., and it's designed to naturally relieve and release tension or stress. Conscious toning is another matter.

This is an essential element that's often overlooked.

In his book, *Brain States*, Tom Kenyon writes, ". . . consciousness is what enlivens sound into information, be it toning of a shaman or the breath-taking movement of a symphony . . . sound as information is created via the agency of consciousness itself." Conscious toning engages the left brain and holds a specific desire or intention. When we tone consciously, the effect is much more powerful in aligning with what exists at the core of our being—resonance.

In So Many Words

Although spoken words are not considered traditional toning, they are vibrations, powerful vibrations, giving form to what we speak. Are you conscious or unconscious about the words you use? My guess is that most of us are unconscious language users. Things pop out of our mouths, and we don't even stop to question whether what we've said or written actually communicates what we consciously intended to communicate. More important, we don't stop to think that what we just said may have an impact beyond the words. *"Just kidding"* is a common tagline to the vicious swipe of sarcastic humor. But what are we really saying? What we fail to realize is that we have just unleashed a chemical reaction in both our body and that of the listener.

The energy of words lingers long after the words themselves are spoken and may become something we had no intention of creating. Fear, self-doubt, and blame may not be felt or seen right away, but the impact will show itself some time in the near or distant future. There are unconscious messages and powerful frequencies coming through in our spoken words. Words matter. We transfer value, meaning, and purpose through our words, launching them into the vibrational reality in which we live. In essence, we are creating our future in this present moment, thought by thought, word by word.

If you want to see what your thoughts were like yesterday, look at your body today. If you want to see what your body will be like tomorrow, look at your thoughts today.

Indian Proverb

Speaking Volumes

All words, spoken consciously or unconsciously, will either strengthen or weaken us. The impact is palpable. For example, I have seen people speak themselves into sickness. If we were to sit in a doctor's office and listen to each patient describe his or her physical challenges, we'd hear each story told in clear and specific detail. These people are reciting the litany of their suffering; and even though their conscious intent is to feel better, they're continuing to speak their discomfort or discontent into reality.

The vibration of belief and the energy of emotion become our words, which then inform how we live our lives. Or is it the other way around? Well, it's both. What we believe is what we speak, and what we speak is what we become.

The influence of our words is felt in all systems of the body—the immune system, nervous system, circulatory system, respiratory system, endocrine system, neurological system, as well as the subtle energy of the chakra system. And believe me, they, too, are communicating.

EXERCISE: Snake Breath

Our amazing bodies are temples of possibility. So let's recap the exercises so far. You have consciously touched your breath and dropped your jaw. Now it is time to feel the place where your power lives.

This breath exercise is fundamental for helping the body's muscle-memory reconnect with the diaphragmatic movement of breath.

Sit comfortably with your back supported and your feet flat on the floor in front of you

Lift and extend your chest area.

Soften the belly muscles and jaw.

Inhale a gentle breath through your nose, don't worry about how much air; that will take care of itself. Just inhale gently and on your exhale make the sound of a hissing snake or tea pot. SSSSSSSSSSS Keep this sound going until you run out of all your air.

Repeat this several times concentrating only on breathing out on SSSSSSS.

Congratulations! You have just awakened the sense memory of your natural breathing pattern, the way you would breathe as a child. Though this breathing is effortless, its impact is huge! As you practice, the more you strengthen the muscles that anchor you to your breath, the more you allow a rich vocal tone (when you add sound). This simple breath exercise grounds you in a sense of place, confident, passionate and purposeful.

Energy Follows Thought ... And Word

Anytime we repeatedly speak about our struggles to any and all available ears, we intensify the very problem that's plaguing us. We ensure the outcome will be what we're speaking about—and may not want. The body takes its cue from the energy most dominant in our field and will respond accordingly. Our cells interpret every word and thought as a literal message, without judging if something is good or bad for us. Cells only respond to vibration.

Do you find yourself in the same situations, with the same types of people, doing the same things again and again, and wondering, *why does this keep happening to me?* Listen to your words. You're giving voice to your expectations, thus recreating the same scenarios.

Not all speech is the same, however. Our language can either stop the flow of our productivity or increase it. Limited beliefs stay active because we feed them by speaking them over and over. **I want** (a belief in not having); **I can't** (a belief in our limitations); **I tried** (a belief in our ineffectiveness) are words that give consent to a lie, a story that empowers the victim within.

Now that you are aware of words you don't want, here are a few words you might use to replace the limiting ones.

I have! I create! I can! I choose! I am! I enjoy!
I love! I do! I live! I see! I know!
I act! I feel! I speak! I am heard!

Experience the power and potential in these words. These statements have life force. They draw you closer than you've ever been to getting everything you've ever wanted. These are powerful words. Speak them out loud, passionately. When you mean what you say and say what you mean with emotional clarity and specificity, what you say will materialize.

There is nothing either good or bad, but thinking makes it so.

William Shakespeare
Hamlet, Act II, Scene 2

But it only *starts* there. Not only are you communicating with others, you are communicating with yourself, your subconscious. The value of speaking from a place of conscious choice is to speak a language no longer limited by right or wrong, good or bad. Instead, you speak from your highest choice. Your voice carries consciousness itself. So, when it's in alignment with subconscious knowing, the effect of your words will dramatically alter your reality. And your reality becomes a vibrational vortex that strengthens everyone.

EXERCISE: Sounding Ahhhhhh

A "magical" tone that can reset your day (and your vibration) is the sound of *ahhhhh*. Why not open your mouth wide and say *ahhhhh*.

1. Stay comfortable.
2. Check and make certain that you relax your tongue and the muscles in your neck and face.
3. Open your mouth (a couple of fingers wide). In a mid-range pitch that feels easy for you, begin to tone *ahhhhh*.
4. Stay with this tone until you run out of air. It is important to complete the tone in one breath.
5. Repeat for a minute or so.
6. At some point, pause and notice how your body feels. Do you feel a little more peaceful? Vibrant? Grounded?

"But," you might argue, *"I think positive thoughts all the time! I even build altars filled with my intentions. Still, my bank account is thin!* OR *My body is too big!* OR *People still take advantage of me!"* If you acknowledge the disconnection between what you desire and what you have, you are seeing the gaping truth of what you expect or believe is possible for you.

Here is that all-important word, alignment. Sound fills that gap, aligns you with your highest truth, and allows you to accept what you desire. It becomes your reality.

Yes, sound that comes from your own voice is the energetic bridge between your head and your heart, your desire and your expectation, your truth and the story you've believed was true. Know that when you choose to speak your passion—aligned with knowing that all of life's good fortunes are your destiny—your words will change the world, one person at a time, one idea at a time, one heartbeat at a time. It's the language of power and choice emerging from the entire field of possibility.

Sound, even the simple sound of ahhhh, soothes your tensions and restores your natural resonance and internal rhythms, which are naturally aligned with the earth's magnetic field itself. The earth's magnetic field vibrates at approximately 7.8 cycles per second. When you're stressed, you tend to vibrate much higher or lower than that. Sound harmonizes and synchronizes body rhythms to help maintain *flow* with the planet itself. Most

It is not what you see, but what you've projected. It's not what you've felt, but what you've decided. It's not what you've experienced, but how you've remembered it. It's not what you've forged, but what you've allowed. And it's not who's appeared, but who you've summoned.

Andy and Mike Dooley
© TUT.com®

of us are acutely aware of how other people sound, from raspy to elegant to sensual—the shrill politician, the booming brother-in-law, the regional dialect. But unless we have laryngitis or catch ourselves on tape, we take our own voices for granted, believing it to be just another bodily function. Alas, there is so much more to you as a voice.

Now is a good time to meet all the parts of your instrument, your personal sound system, the one that will help you restore harmony, clear energy blocks, create joy, and possibly save your life in the process. To start, see if you can eavesdrop on yourself. How fully do you breathe when you speak? Are you nasal? Full-throated? Piercing? Is your voice resonant and compelling? Do you run out of breath, hesitate, trail off at the end of a thought?

What we know or feel about ourselves is recreated daily through the resonance of our voice. Fear, tension, and stress all reshape our skeletal structure and our musculature, rewire our brains, and find their way out of our mouths through the tone of our voice.

How does the tone of your voice change, depending on whether you are happy, confused, resentful, hopeful, angry or sad . . .? How connected are you to your words, or the feelings (physical or emotional) behind what you say? Do you say what you mean? Do you feel what you say? Are you clear and specific? How do the words you choose affect you? How do they affect others? Just notice and don't judge.

Voice is the only artistic experience, which is both finite and infinite at the same time. It is fallible and fragile, gone in an instant unseen, only felt. It is remembered from the past, even a long moment ago. Anticipated, sensing its future even as its present is just occurring. It's temporal, visceral, organic. Such a complex, simple and beguiling transcendent state.

Arthur Samuel Joseph
1980

In addition to rediscovering the sound, or tone, of your voice, I invite you to once again pay attention to the way you hold your mouth or jaw. Often we perceive our mouths as wide open when they are actually tiny slits. This is the one universal physical feature across the spectrum of jaws and voices I've worked with over the years. For many, a wide-open mouth happens only at the dentist. Not always a positive sensory memory. The nakedness of an open mouth can make some feel like they might be too exposed, even losing control. They're not aware they are containing themselves and their facial expressions until I ask them to try something different. That tightness is part of their communication, both seen and heard.

Compare, if you will, your voice to a signal tower pulsing frequencies through the Universe, much like a radio broadcasts radio waves. Nothing stops the movement of these frequencies. *Sound is the most powerful force in the Universe.* So, too, is your voice.

The sound of your voice can soothe a frightened child, halt a bully in his or her tracks, or provide encouragement, empathy, or compassion to a friend or nation. I would say that is real power. As I mentioned earlier, your voice is more than a sine wave; *your voice is a carrier wave of consciousness itself.*

Reclaiming My Power

Consider my own healing journey. Doctors offered indisputable medical evidence that my prognosis was dismal. They claimed my time was limited and I should get my affairs in order. Not what anyone wants to hear! By this time, however, I was not in resistance to them or their science. I simply agreed with their data as a paradigm or perspective, as a reflection of their truth, but not *my* truth.

In contrast, I knew I was not a victim, which meant I was free to create my own paradigm, one that would exist alongside their American Medical model and serve me as a whole, healthy person. My alternate paradigm allowed me to have a dominant thought in alignment with my truth. I would verbalize this truth daily, not with the hope of being cured in my future, but with the knowing that I already embodied that reality. My statement was: *"I am in a state of well-being. All is well."*

Daily, this mantra carried me through the dog days of chemo. And even when I was flat out on my back, weakened by the chemicals, hair falling out, and with little energy for work, I knew I was in a state of well-being . . . all was well. Every cell in my body agreed with me. Because this was my dominant thought, my cells were allowed the energetic freedom to function *as* wellbeing.

Through the process of entrainment, sound can transform negative, repressed emotions into a state of psychological equanimity that has direct and immediate effects on our physiology. Sonic entrainment can also restore harmony between our innermost selves—our essence—and the universe, thus reawakening our spiritual consciousness.

Dr. Mitchell L. Gaynor
The Healing Power of Sound: Recovery from Life-Threatening Illness Using Sound, Voice, and Music.
Shambhala, 2002. p. 64

Sound Tracks Of Self-Healing

The sound of our voices has the power to shift our thoughts from the past or future to NOW through vibration. The secret is *entrainment.*

A great example of entrainment is found in the swing of two metronomes in the same vicinity. If they begin slightly out of sync with each other, in a short time they find a mutual rhythm and keep the same time. The same is true for the systems of the body. Our muscular, nervous, respiratory, and circulatory systems all vibrate in a set rhythm. If we get off-kilter, we have the ability to use our voice to entrain the rhythms of our body and restore balance to the whole body system.

Everything is vibration in perpetual motion, and every molecule of our being acts as a magnet, drawing to us experiences in resonance with our own dominant vibration. That includes the entrainment of each organ to the unique codes imbedded in the sounds of your voice.

Ever notice that if you pluck a string of a guitar or violin, the other strings vibrate in sympathetic oscillation with the plucked string, which has become the dominant pulse. That same sympathetic oscillation happens throughout your biology. You also feel it in the rhythms of the moon cycles or as you cycle through seasons. Your body responds to the dominant pulse it's exposed to.

When using the voice to create a sound, the brain responds by locking on to the pulse, shifting the brainwave into a deeply relaxed state. New neural pathways are created, overriding the old programs of behavior and belief. All your systems balance in a matter of seconds. With dominant harmonious frequencies created by your voice and your thoughts, the natural rhythm and frequency for all your body systems are restored and you continue to hum along. You feel good.

Giving voice to your thoughts amplifies the power of the thoughts, making your thoughts vibrate with greater radiance and speed. When you enhance the quality and force of your thoughts by speaking them, your entire field changes. You voice your choice, taking center stage, no longer hiding in the wings of desire. You have taken flight.

Your Body Speaks Its Mind. Are You Listening?

Feeling and emotion are the gateway to transformation. Serious power. Our bodies are forever offering us direct guidance to this power—pulsing, throbbing, at times painful, peaceful, joyful, stressful, lonely—a 3D language of physical or emotional signals that can be interpreted as 100 percent literal, like a first-grade primer . . . if we are willing to notice.

Innate intelligence is encoded in the cellular structure of our bodies, but do we know what to listen for? Do we understand the language the cell is using? And, even if we did, would we know what to do with the information? The questions and the answers are immediate as an experience, a sensation, an emotion, if we pay attention.

If you could feel the vibration of your own heart beating, how would you know it? Could you identify it, intentionally? Without feeling the sensation or pulse, you can't fully experience your physical self in the moment. What are you really feeling? What do you want in this moment? How do you tune in, right at this moment—do you hear your body answering, humming, surging ... or buzzing?

Stay tuned.

Emotion is the chief source of all becoming conscious. There can be no transforming of darkness into light and of apathy into movement without emotion.

C. G. Jung
Psychologist

Emotional Guidance—The Shortest Road Home

The body is like a seismograph. When something needs to shift, it will give us signals, hundreds of signals, letting us know that change is knocking. It can be subtle or in our face—a nagging irritation, a trail of emotional upsets, real physical pain or disease. All signal imbalance. And this imbalance won't go away simply by wishing it away or denying it exists. In fact, the more we resist or deny something, the more it persists.

If we've spent a lifetime denying our emotions, editing our feelings, and silencing our voices, we may argue, *But wait. Feelings are impractical, messy, awkward, LOUD!* This argument stems from our inability—even our unwillingness—to balance or contain our emotions. If we have not cultivated the language of emotion from our childhood, we are threatened by these emotions, unwilling to feel ourselves as sensate beings. We become rigid, unyielding to change, and just plain stuck. The thought of allowing pleasure or feeling the sensations of our aliveness can be terrifying. In terms of the subtle body, this develops into a second chakra issue (see Chapter 6).

If only we would give ourselves permission to feel the raw, unfiltered visceral, authentic data of our experiences, we'd awaken the unconscious reaction firing off extremely important information throughout the whole body. Our emotions are part of the sensory information that organize and interpret these raw feelings, our unconscious reaction. Our conscious awareness allows us to use these valuable sensory tools becoming our emotional intelligence, providing us with emotional guidance.

Imagine that you feel slighted by someone or some situation. There are two ways to move with this. One is to look the other way, say nothing, and stuff it . . . until something unrelated triggers you and you blow your top. Or you could recognize the feeling first as a sensation (stomach churning, throat closing, heat rising) and allow your emotional intelligence to interpret what's really going on.

If you let it, your authentic raw feeling will lead you to what belief is being triggered. Maybe you feel inadequate in the situation, or put down by a superior, or just lost. Trust that your emotional guidance will help you choose the next step, from sensation to solution. You simply have to ask. *What will bring me the most peace?* The answer will always come.

Don't ask yourself what the world needs, ask yourself what makes you come alive, and do that. Because what the world needs is people who have come alive.

Dr. Howard Thurman
Author and
civil rights leader

Of course, human beings are a complex combination of sensations, feelings, and emotions so I encourage you to listen to your own heart and allow your unique guidance seed your choices. Your innate guidance system is the fundamental body wisdom that brings order to the chaos that's been created. When you allow ourselves to experience the sensations of life, you build the language of feeling. This is fundamental to creating value, integrity, and meaning in your live.

In fact, this emotional information wakes up the cells of the body, like an indicator light signaling something important is going on. Pay attention! What stirs within is more than what you may think is going on. Remember that your emotions are part of an elaborate guidance system poised to transport you to deeper understanding and higher ground.

Frustration, overwhelm, confusion, anger, or incandescent rage—all are allies ready to introduce you to your power. Creating so much chaos forces us to ask the hard questions so you can discover your own truth.

Feeling angry? Sit with it. Experience it. Give it a voice. Let it shout. Ignite every cell in your body with the force of your voice. Move from vague, limp intention to an image so lucid, it's emblazoned in the heavens. So what if feelings are messy. So is ice cream in the hands of a child and it's worth the mess! Besides, your feelings are the most loyal partners you've ever had . . . and ever denied. They provide the best navigational system available. An invaluable bonus!

Your emotions make it possible to connect with the "stuff" you've buried so very long, stuff that obstructs the flow of your life. They urge you to leap fearlessly to new understanding. So feel them and you'll create a passageway to the next best place. Choosing to use your voice, your sound, to carry you through the tunnel of fear and into the light yields the highest return—the emotion of *joy*.

Yes, feeling good is a constant choice in every moment; it's your spiritual bottom line.

Living Out Loud

Theater Becomes The Key

Boston was a hub for new theater and the Om Theatre Company was the calm at my center, laying new theatrical ground and stretching me beyond comfort. The Om offered a theater experience that demanded the whole person show up, be seen, felt, and heard. Whether you were audience or actor, on or off the stage, your presence was necessary. At the core of Om, the Sufi tradition wove sweet soul through the ensemble work. Sufism, as I mentioned earlier, was ballast in my emotional storm. Still keeping the madness of my alcoholism under wraps, I could walk upon this holy stage and somehow feel safe. Some called it sacred theater. I called it home.

The year 1980 marked the end of my drinking/drugging career. Beer, wine, cigarettes, cocaine—all old friends—now turned on me. This game was over. Deciding to become sober was the easy part. When you have nothing more to lose, the choices are crystal clear and simple. Had I known the challenges I'd face living sober, I might have turned and run.

Still, I managed to string two sober years together, accept an acting job in San Francisco, and move my life to the city by the Bay. I was up for it, or so I thought. However, a week before the show opened, this tiny progressive theater lost its funding and the show was cancelled. I stood at the epicenter of my own private earthquake and had to deal with the rubble. I panicked. I had *nothing* except a signed lease for the empty studio I'd just rented for the run of the show. No income!

On the evening of October 10, 1983, frustrated, rudderless, and broke, I let loose an awkward prayer. *"If You really do exist, I expect You to tell me why I am here, right now!"* And in case the Universe didn't hear me, I demanded once more, *"WHY AM I HERE? I want answers! And I don't want any subtle blue-feather-type thing that I have to find and interpret. I want a MACK-truck sign! Do you hear me? It's gotta hit me in the face so hard, I WON'T miss the*

For years one works and wants to know more, to acquire more skill, but in the end one has to reject it all and not learn but unlearn, not to know how to do, but how not to do, and always face doing; to risk total defeat; not a defeat in the eyes of others, which is less important, but the defeat of a missed gift, an unsuccessful meeting with someone, that is to say an unsuccessful meeting with oneself.

Jerzy Grotowski
Lecture at New York University, 1970.
Translated by Boleslaw Taborski, 1972

message." I then brushed my teeth and went to bed.

The next morning, October 11 at 4:30 a.m., in came the response. Two clear scenes of young, sober alcoholics engaged in a dramatic exchange were taking shape in my dreamtime. My eyes popped open. I bolted out of bed with that disoriented early morning shudder. *"Oh my God, this is it! This is what I'm here to do!"* My prayer was answered, and . . . now what?

In 1984, I birthed the peer-to-peer alcohol and drug prevention program in San Francisco, making live theater the vehicle for addressing the crushing realities of addiction among young people. For nearly 20 years, I had the privilege of working with 20 different casts of young people, all of whom changed thousands of lives, young and old, performing before millions in both live performance and television. The original company, based in San Francisco, was titled Teens Kick Off (TKO). It was then replicated in Seattle as Coming 2 and replicated for the final time in Tucson as Coming To.

The road to the first performance was fraught with challenges. Sober students were hard to come by. Colleagues thought I was crazy. Many times I agreed with them. I continued to confront the Universe, firing off questions, making demands and waiting for answers. What surprised me most was that answers always came. This was my first experience with co-creation, although that word had yet to enter my lexicon.

As the creative process unfolded, the burden became clear. What kind of artistic process could be sustained though each cast? What process would be safe and nurturing for the young actors and help them discover their personal truth, and also be artistically strong? Doubt shadowed me. "What was I thinking? I'm only an actor, not a director. I've never run a nonprofit before, much less raised funds to support a company! I've never even written a script!" Overwhelmed, I turned my thoughts to the Universe. "Do you know who you're dealing with here? I don't know anything about what is being asked of me! Is it possible you might have dropped the dream at the wrong address?" A quiet came over me, and I heard a calm inner voice say, "Just put one foot in front of the other; I will do the rest." What the . . . ?

In my dream the angel shrugged and said, 'If we fail this time it will be a failure of imagination,' And then she placed the world gently in the palm of my hand.

Brian Andreas
Artist

Now, I have no special "powers" but I was certain that something had just told me to keep going and doors would open. So I did . . . and they did.

Still plagued by doubt, I wondered, "How am I ever going to direct these non-actors to be authentic in performance?" If they were to influence their peers, their primary audience, they'd have to do one thing very well—be fearless truth-tellers to their audiences and to themselves.

This was a tall order for newly sober alcoholic teens. For anyone, really. The process would have to cultivate strength—spiritual, physical, emotional, and mental. Feeling limited by traditional theater exercises, I knew I needed an experience that allowed them to bypass the filters of the ego and tap the well of cellular memory, the place of creation. This was where their authentic stories lived. This I knew.

During one rehearsal, my attention was drawn to the students as they prepared for their creative work, yet I was struck by how detached they were from the energy in their bodies. Their body parts moved around, but their essence wasn't at all connected to their movements. For a performance to influence audiences, the actors must be moved emotionally.

The body is our instrument, our creative source. So when I noticed how locked into robotic, mindless movement the students were, I encouraged them to explore something. "See if you can put sound on that movement!" I urged. My instruction was intended to give the body (or body part) its own voice. By including the actors' voice along with their bodies, their creative expression became dynamic and compelling, not to mention cathartic. The exercise came alive! The students came alive! The "feeling" information coming through their sounds was incredibly honest. I could actually hear the tension in their necks and shoulders by how the sound was being expressed. If the sound was authentic—that is, deeply connected to the tissue—it had a different quality, a different resonance, than if they were going through the motions of producing a sound and moving a body part.

To my surprise and great delight, the quality of their work changed dramatically. Because sound revealed depth and dimension to a simple movement, the quality of their emotional work deepened. Soon it became obvious that adding sound was so much more than theatrical. Sound was *therapeutic*. The change was palpable.

Only when you truly inhabit your body can you begin the healing journey.

Gabrielle Roth
Social artist and dancer

A short time later, I stumbled on an old box marked Boston Theatre. Randomly thrown inside were old scripts, notes, "important" scraps of paper—all from Om Theatre Company some 10 years earlier. Then it appeared. Scribbled on the back of a ringed binder were seven vowel sounds and the word *chakra* scrawled on the side. These sound notes were from a day the

Sufi Healing Order came to an Om rehearsal expressly to teach these tones. The memory returned and I saw clear the way to authenticity. Here was the actor tool—the transformation tool—I had been hoping for.

With the cornerstone for the artistic process in place, we could now build something of real substance and create living art for social change. The sounds I shared with the students were incorporated into our daily warm-up routine—for rehearsal, for performance, for life.

To teach is to learn twice.

Joseph Joubert
French essayist

Over the course of a year, sound would carry them through an impressive panoply of challenges—personal, social, emotional, and theatrical—while strengthening their physical recovery. What surprised me most was how confident the students were becoming. Sound grounded them in their own skin, allowing them to travel safely and easily through any emotional landscape and maintain balance. They recognized that *they were not their pain,* and that emotions are mutable, reprogrammable electrical charges that they could change. They discovered within themselves the power to choose how they perceived their lives and that they could consciously influence outcomes through the power of their voice.

I would watch as they would disarm audiences and open doors for others, simply by being themselves. Their true power was anchored in their willingness and courage to tell the truth. They had become athletes of the heart. And its effectiveness was proven in a 1990 evaluation of Teens Kick Off (TKO) by researchers at Stanford University and its Department of Education. Remarkably, within six months of seeing a Teens Kick Off performance, 21 percent of every audience either got sober themselves or directly influenced a friend or family member to seek recovery.

In 2000, during my final cast of my final year, I was told that, given how fast the hepatitis C virus was mutating, I could probably expect to live another year or so. At that point, having exhausted all treatment options, I turned to those seven tones. If sound could transform these young people into confident, emotionally whole, integrated, spiritually strong truth-tellers, what might sound do for me? It was time for the teacher to be taught. I was ready.

SoundShifting® – The Process

Sound healing is the conscious use of sound to create an environment that allows healing within the physical, mental, emotional, or spiritual aspects of our being.

Sound*Shifting*® is a technique that uses the innate power of the human voice to create a conscious, expansive vibrational pathway to whole-body health, balancing the chakra system along with all other systems of the dense body.

The goal in sound healing is to restore resonance—a word often used but rarely understood. *Resonance* is the fundamental frequency with which any object vibrates in its natural state. It means coherency and flow within the frequencies of the whole body system. The easiest, most effective way to clear and balance this subtle body system is through toning. It's your voice coupled with focused attention that restores the rhythm and vitality to the chakra as well as the body efficiently and effectively allowing you to tap into a powerful healing current . . . effortlessly.

The body is like a finely tuned orchestra playing your stirring personal symphony in harmony, rhythm, and symmetry. When that harmony is disrupted, it can be compared to a gust of wind blowing the sheet music off the conductor's music stand. What ensues is musical chaos. Though the orchestra plays on, the music is no longer organized in a beautiful way. Instead, it's erratic and inharmonious, with each instrument out of rhythm. In order for the orchestra to get back on track, back in harmony, someone needs to place the sheet music back on the music stand.

Similarly, your voice and the Chakra Tones become tools you can use to restore harmony to your life, tone by tone.

The content of the chakras is formed largely by repeated patterns from our actions in our day-to-day life. . . . Repeated movements and habits create fields in the world around us.

Anodea Judith
Wheels of Life: A Users' Guide to the Chakra System
Llewellyn Publications
1989, p. 24

The Chakra Tones

Your chakras are the invisible, subtle energy centers or vortexes of the body. The word *chakra* comes from the Sanskrit word *chakram* meaning a wheel or revolving disc. They are spirals of life-giving energy that flow through the physical, emotional, and spiritual dimensions of existence. Each of these wheels of power forms a center of activity that receives, assimilates, and expresses life force energy, and each chakra is associated with a particular body function, emotion, color, and sound. Although we have as many chakras as we have cells, for our purpose, we will focus on seven of the most common chakras.

Energy moves through the chakras as both expanding currents (moving up the spine) and grounding currents (moving down into the base of the spine) and impacts all systems within your body—the nervous system, immune system, respiratory system, endocrine systems, and circulatory, ever expanding beyond the physical structure of your body into the psychological, emotional, and spiritual energy systems.

At different times in your life, various chakras are more open and balanced than others. Lifestyle patterns can make the chakra sluggish or stuck, while others can even become displaced, still connected but floating completely outside of the dense body. Clearly, chakra health depends on the type of mental or emotional beliefs or "programs" you're running.

Only your own vocal cords can produce the unique set of harmonics and overtones which are characteristic of your personal, unique voice-print pattern—a pattern highly recognizable to the part of your biological system which designed and grew your body out of two cells in the first place. This part of the unconscious mind designed the vocal cords themselves and deeply recognizes the unique frequency pattern of sound that they produce.

Dr. Jeffrey Thompson
Director of the Center for Neuroacoustic Research

We don't need to revisit how those old programs are established (covered earlier in this book) but if you notice you feel stuck in a never-ending loop of behaviors or patterns that don't feel good, sounding the Chakra Tones will begin to shift the energy, changing not only how you feel, but how your chakras function as well.

A Chakra Tone is an open, primordial vowel tone that resonates a specific chakra area or energy center. When I speak of primordial, I'm referring to sounds that originate as part of ancient tonal language. But I'm also referring to the organic nature of sound as a primordial experience inside the womb. After all, these sensations form our first language—the rhythms and vibrations of life itself. Even though our eyes are closed and fluids fill our cavities, our sensory experience stays with us, implanting deep rhythms and vibrations into the cells of our developing body. The Chakra Tones are what activates our subconscious, sensory language.

When toning with intention, your sound forms an energetic grid through which previously blocked energy can move. Each chakra is an activation point, with the sound of your voice acting as the accelerator that engages the innat wisdom encoded in the cells.

It may be difficult to believe that this invisible subtle body energy system has such power over your health and sense of harmony. Yet, it does. When freed from oppressive programs, it is an energy system that is exceedingly efficient and complex. It sends energy out from the core of your being and draws energy back in again, assimilating the currents that liberate and manifest while expanding life energies that activate a higher consciousness. How high can you go? As high as you choose to go.

Not only is toning with intention one of the most powerful ways to shift the patterns of those unwanted beliefs, it is also shifting the energetic patterns in the neural network associated with any given belief.

Like changing the radio dial on your car stereo, toning allows you to change a frequency of disharmony to a frequency of ease and well-being in a very short period of time. Most people report feeling an immediate sense of calm coupled with a sense of clarity when they do this.

Change for each of us will look different; what is right for you will not be right for someone else. If we want to create significant change, speaking about it and thinking new thoughts is only a beginning. Unless we shift the vibrations of beliefs locked in place throughout our body/brain, we will continue to act out the old behavior patterns.

Prepare to travel deeper into the journey of sound. You're about to focus with such clear intention that your body will start to move itself into its own natural resonance. To best produce these tones and maximize their resonance, posture and pitch is everything.

CHAKRA OVERVIEW

The Posture

There are only two things to be done, the necessary and the impossible.

Ibn'l Arabi
Sufi mystic

It's important to remember that having an aligned posture is crucial for sound and breath to move well though your body. If you're sitting with rolled, hunched shoulders, ribs caved in and neck sticking out like a turkey, only a tiny stream of sound can move through your body with little effect.

For best results, sit in your chair or on the floor with the small of your back flush against your seat back or wall. Gently let your pelvic cradle tilt forward so you feel your sit bones against the base of your chair. Extend your upper body, imagining a little cord attached to your chest bone, lifting and extending the spine upward, chin dropped toward chest. Get acquainted with this amazing feeling. It is your power posture.

Make conscious contact with the bones, tissue, and muscle movement as you reach for the heavens. Your spine supports your breath, which supports your voice, allowing the freeing/healing process to begin. As you extend the spine, let your belly muscles soften and breathe naturally. This allows you to breathe deeply from the diaphragm. It also provides stronger, fuller breath support, making the tones full and resonant. Relax and breathe from the diaphragm and stay aware of the extended spine. As you engage the sound, maintain as relaxed a state as you can.

The goal is to allow the laws of nature—that is, physical gravity and alignment—to be the foundation for your shifting states of awareness.

The Pitch

The pitch or tone is preceded by a quiet stillness—listen and allow. Your body knows the resonant pitch harmonically structured for each chakra within your body. While there are some systems of chakra balancing that use specific musical notes for each chakra, not all agree. So go with what feels like the right sound for you.

I suggest you start with the lowest tone you can make for your Root Chakra and gradually move up the scale, so to speak, and you will be fine. Your body will let you know that you have "hit" the right tone because a) you will feel it, and b) it will seem easy to produce.

Spend no time or energy judging and doubting how you sound. . . . *Is it right? Is it wrong?* Instead, feel the tone vibrate in the chakra point where you're focused. That feeling sensation i confirmation that energy is moving. You may feel it as heat or a tingling, pulsing sensation. If so, *great!* If you can't feel it at first that's normal. Be patient; eventually you'll feel it.

The Metho

Because the Root Chakra is the first tone on our chakra sp ral, it's often the most challenging to create. I mean, how man of us spend much time contemplating their tailbone, much les sounding it? So I want to walk you through the method of mak ing this first tone. The others will come easily.

The sound for the root chakra is a deep resonant *uuh,* as if you are saying the word *muuuud*. The placement of the tongue is important to make this tone resonate. You want to slide the tongue toward the back of the throat. This loosens the vocal folds and widens the back of the throat, allowing you to produce a sound much lower than your normal "low" voice. It also opens the air passage from the diaphragm through the mouth. Your sound will end up reminding you of a foghorn. If you feel tension in your neck and your sound is "stuck," you can unblock the passageway all the way to the diaphragm by imagining your own inner body spaciousness.

Voicing Tips

One way to feel the expanse in your throat is to imagine being startled but without making any vocal sound. That startled sucking sound on the inhalation "uuuh" drops the tongue back and opens the throat.

Another tip is to gently drop your head as far back as comfortable without crunching your discs or involving your shoulders. Picture a wide open channel where the geyser of breath and sound can come from deep within, *haaaaaaaaaaaa.* Don't try to engage your throat, just let the sound rise from your belly and out your mouth. Now gently bring your head back to center and feel how your belly muscles engage as you make the sound of *huh-huh-huh-huh-huh* coming from your diaphragm. Repeat a few times until you feel your voice come to life and you are able to relax into the warm pool of vibrations spinning in your diaphragm.

Sound/Body Mechanics

Since this Root chakra vibrates at a very low tone, the support needs to come from the muscles in the diaphragm. You might give a slight grab or thrust at the beginning of the sound, gradually constricting your abdominal muscles as your voice travels on your air. Maintain that support as you sustain the sound all the way to the end of the breath . . . until that last bit of breath is wrung from your body. Then watch as your body delivers another miracle of life; you will inhale. This breath will automatically be drawn in from the depth of that "empty place" filling you with life itself, over and over again. How wonderful that you are no long waiting to exhale.

Color is an added frequency if you are someone who easily "sees" color. Allow the thought of a deep, rich red (Root Chakra) warm your lower body as you focus on your tailbone. Remember to stay relaxed and allow your mouth to fall open (at least the width of one finger). Hold your intention on an open, vibrating lower body area, and tone. UUH...UUH...UUH...

Once you finish with the tone, keep you eyes closed and your attention on the chakra. Your attention allows you to listen to the sensation of the sound in your body. Feel the vibration, the tingling, maybe even heat. Silence is as important as creating the sound itself. It brings you into deeper contact with the sensation of sound and its expanse. The body actually feels more spacious. Notice how your energy moves throughout the chakra you are focusing on. See the sound move . . . and just listen.

THE CHAKRA TONES

1st Chakra – Root Chakra

Placement - tailbone

Color - deep red

Sound - UUH (sounds like 'mud') – tongue slips back in throat to loosen vocal folds and create a rich, round sound.; gently thrust as you begin the tone, using abdominal muscles to support the sound and breath as it slides from your mouth.

Area of Impact – rectum, lower intestines, legs, feet, knees and releases stress in lower back.

The element for the Root Chakra is earth. It concerns itself with our solid connection to Self, the roots of our survival, our bodies and our physical health. Instinctively we know we have a right to exist, to occupy space, to establish our identity, to care for ourselves.

The root chakra represents our sense of security. Fundamental to our security is knowing our basic needs are met. The root chakra demands we pay serious attention to these needs. Imagine yourself "having" something as basic as home, money, food, and friendship, fundamental to a healthy root system. Our capacity to focus and manifest what is our birthright sits in this powerful chakra and is the foundation of our sense of self-trust and capacity for self-nurturance.

Root Chakra Meditation Exercise
I HAVE

Take a moment to feel your body. Feel it breathe in . . . and out. Feel your heart beating inside, the moisture in your mouth, the food in your belly. Explore the space your body occupies—height, weight, width. Feel the weight of your body on the floor or chair.

Ask your body how it feels. Is it tired, refreshed, relieved? Listen to the answer.

Begin your journey by going down into your body. Sinking deeply into the base of the spine, you find a warm red glowing sphere of energy. Imagine this deep red energy flowing down your legs . . . through your knees . . . into your feet. Feel it run through your feet and into the floor beneath you, through the floor and down into the core of the Earth. Feel this cord of energy as an anchor, settling you, calming you, grounding you.

Think of the things you HAVE, the food that nourishes you, the house in which you find safety and shelter. The Winds, Waters and Trees of this Earth.

Think of the financial abundance you have. Whatever the amount, it is a gift from the Earth. Watch as this money evolves into even greater abundance, filling every corner of your being. Feel the joy of this Abundance. This abundant stream of life is flowing into you and out of you, through your hands, your feet, your heart and your mind. Feel each cell radiate the truth of this abundant life. YOU ARE THE SOURCE OF ALL [illegible] AND UNDERSTANDING.

Feel its expression in your throat, its recognition in your vision, its imprint in your mind. Place your awareness on your tail-bone, the Root chakra, take a deep belly breath and allow the sound vibrations to magnify this abundant reality.

st Chakra Tone: UUH

Affirmation for Root Chakra:

I accept and love my body more and more every day and in every way. I deserve . . . I now release all fears that may have blocked my participation and creation with all things. . . I let go with Love and allow nature to support me more and more. I now allow only things that enhance my life or give me joy.

2nd Chakra - Sacral Chakra

Placement – mid-abdomen, between naval and pubic bone
Color – orange
Sound - OOH (a long, strong, sustained 'oh' sound)
Area of Impact – colon, prostrate and ovarian health; make this sound with strong support from the abdominal muscles as they gradually constrict to sustain vocal strength; unlocks stress stored in sacral or mid-back area

The element of this second chakra is water. The center of sensation, feelings, emotions, pleasure, intimacy, movement and connection with self and others are all part of the authentic self and basic to this chakra. It also speaks to our capacity to be in the flow, to experience the ever-present reality of change and expansion of consciousness. Physically the reproductive organs, large intestines, ovaries and testes are all influenced by the energetic flow of the second chakra. Sensations, the building blocks of feelings and emotions, are important for our connection to Self and the world around us.

Pleasure, another essential feature of this chakra, is responsible for the health of the physical body, the rejuvenation of the spirit and the healing of our personal/social/cultural/environmental relationships.

Sacral Chakra Meditation Exercise
I FEEL

As the breath moves through your nose, throat, and lungs your abdomen expands. It ebbs and flows as evenly and gracefully as waves upon a shore. Back and forth, empty and full . . in and out.

Deep in your belly you become aware of the warm glow o ORANGE, pulsing through your pelvis, through your ab domen, through your hips, through your thighs . . . flowin through your belly and up through your back to nourish all o you.

You greet yourself! You honor yourself! You are alive!

Gently place your hands on you mid-abdomen. Stay cor scious of the touch and begin to gently rotate your hips in a ci cle while you sit. Sway back and forth, creating a rhythmi motion. Feel the wave of motion that yields emotion—a feelin a yearning, a thought, a sensation—the building-blocks of co sciousness itself. Ever shifting, ever churning, ever expandin You are in a state of constant change.

Experience the pleasure and enthusiastic joy remembering that YOU are the flow, that YOU embody perfect health, that YOU are conscious alignment with Source, that all your relationships are becoming more life-giving and life-supporting.

Take a deep breath into the belly, place your awareness approximately two inches below your navel. Allow the sound frequencies to heal the emotions of the past and restore resonance and passion to your life.

2nd Chakra Tone: OOH

Affirmation for Sacral Chakra:

I am continually in a state of well-being as I listen to and honor my deepest needs and desires. . . I feel good about myself. It is safe to experience pleasure . . . I allow the pleasures of life to unfold before me and I enjoy all the benefits of such pleasures.

3rd Chakra - Solar Plexus

Placement - base of the sternum
Color - yellow
Sound - EEH (like 'head') or AYE (as in 'egg') the mouth is drawn wide across the face; it is supported by the muscle group just at the base of the sternum, as muscles constrict the "gravel" sound moves on the breath out of the mouth. Keep throat open.
Area of Impact – stomach, spleen, gallbladder, liver, pancreas, kidney

... metabolism. The ... 'little will" or ego will, but the Divine will is the ocus for this chakra. The energy within the Solar Plexus is an ntense sense of identity, a personal power, a formidable power. We strengthen the inner intuitive self and trust one's gut, which s how we recognize our connection to Creation. That instinct rings us into alliance with honoring ourselves, knowing how nd where to direct our energy.

Solar Plexus Meditation Exercise
I ACT

You are still, yet you sense a growing, expanding warmth ithin. There is awareness here and it is awakening. From a place of stillness you call on the Self. You awaken another part of the journey . . . expanding . . . returning to Source within. You call upon the Self through your will, and it rises to your call.

Your solar plexus is a vital intersection of energy . . . a merging, weaving web of power . . . like a fire, growing higher and brighter. You begin to remember that with every breath you are growing in alliance with Divine Source. "I and thee are one." Power flows through you naturally, easily, calmly. More and more you recognize that YOU are the one with the power. YOU choose what goes on around you and within you.

It becomes easier to remember this power—to remember its vitality, its purpose and strength as it ignites your will to act. You open to it more and more. You allow it in, and you pass it on naturally, effortlessly, willingly, joyfully. Exhilarated, your body relaxes. The decisions you make for your life are clearer and clearer.

You again return to the gentle breathing . . . in . . . and out . . . in . . . and out. On the next breath, place your awareness at the base of your sternum where the ribs meet and begin to activate the fires of intense self-identity. More and more, you are at home in your own skin.

3rd Chakra Tone - EEH

Affirmation for Solar Plexus Chakra:

I am now choosing to act upon my power to change and direct my life... I claim my power without diminishing others... I am confident in my ability to make the most of my life, therefore I am a success in whatever I choose to do . . . in every moment I know I am free to choose.

4th Chakra - Heart Chakra

Placement - center of breast bone

Color – green

Tone – AAH (sounds like 'awe') - mouth open two fingers wide producing a more refined and gentle sound; sound is supported by diaphragmatic breath and softer than previous chakra tones.

Area of Impact – heart and breast; supports improved immune function, stress reduction, lower blood pressure

The element associated with this Chakra is Air. Physically, this chakra impacts the heart area and the lungs and reflects the soft touch of spirit active in our lives, our spiritual center. Our own hearts are designed to express beauty, compassion, acceptance, forgiveness and love. It is against our spiritual nature to act otherwise. The Heart Chakra is the center of the energetic body, just as love is the center our lives. What we seek in this sound activation is a kind of serenity and peace, which is what comes to us when we untangle the web of resentment, pain and anger from our hearts. The spiritual goal of this chakra is to live in balance—to live in a state of grace, of delicacy, of gentleness.

The sound of this chakra allows one to become more lighthearted, where your heart-centered essence can pour through. It is a condition of being at one with the deep core of our emotions and no longer tied to struggle. Self-love is the outcome.

Heart Chakra Meditation Exercise
I LOVE

Deep within the expanse of your own being is the sound of life, the sound of love, the sound of one heart . . . beating . . . beating. Feel its rhythms pumping life through every part of you, renewing you.

Breathe in deeply, drawing in the air...allow its softness, depth and wisdom. As you breathe, spirit awakens your heart-centered essence . . . moving you . . . changing you . . . opening you. You experience a growing awareness of a deep comforting

th Chakra Tone - AAH

Affirmation for Heart Chakra:

As I open my heart to the love within me I experience greater harmony flowing all around me . . . I lead with love . . . I continually allow love to come to me and through me . . . every day I allow more loving acceptance of myself and others . . . more and more I forgive myself and others.

5th Chakra - The Throat Chakra

Placement – throat
Color - sky blue
Tone – OOO (sounds like 'soothe') – soft open jaw with lips shaped into soft round shape; a pure, delicate higher tone; not falsetto
Area of Impact – thyroid, neck, throat

The Throat Chakra is the most delicate center in the human energy system and can be thrown off balance when we do not honor our deepest feelings and express our truth to ourselves and to others. The element is sound. Sound is consciousness.

Physically, this chakra reflects the health of the thyroid and the region of the neck and shoulders. Feeling that what we have to say is valuable and makes a contribution is an important quality for strengthening this center.

Sound is original force. Are we expressing the truth of pure heart-centered speech? Are we listening to deeper guidance, the voice from within?

Throat Chakra Meditation Exercise
I SPEAK, I AM HEARD

If you listen, you can hear it now. It is in your breath, it is in your heart, it is in your own mind, in the rhythm of each and every thought.

Tone the voice that is within you. This is where you must begin. Hear its call, hear its answer in the darkness . . . fear and pain are now released. Thank them, for they have been loyal allies and teachers. Behold the sound of source, the sound of your creation where echoes of primordial sound purify all vibration. Your voice sends forth the frequencies of *your true nature.* If matter is the matrix of Spirit, and Spirit is the higher state of matter, your voice is the Divine Synergy of being . . . sing out the song of your soul. From one sound does it all emerge and to one sound shall it return.

Place your awareness at the base of your throat and allow the pure simplicity of HUUUUUU . . . .

5th Chakra Tone – OOO

Affirmation for Throat Chakra:

Creativity flows as I begin to open to my true nature . . . I find myself speaking from the truth of my radiant being . . . Telling the truth to myself and others is making my relationships deep and meaningful. . . I am responsible for everything I create in my life, and it continues to bring me joy.

6th Chakra - The Brow Chakra or Third Eye

Placement – center of the forehead
Color – indigo
Tone – EEE (Long ē sound through nasal passage and mouth, with attention on the middle of the forehead; place sound forward in the "facial mask" as it moves through sinus area to pineal gland; a higher falsetto tone)
Area of Impact – stimulates pineal gland, etches new neural pathways in brain, greatly reduces (often eliminates) pain due to headaches when gently toning

This Brow Chakra is the spiritual center in which we trust our deep insights and use our imaginations to see what and who we truly are. The element of this chakra is Light and the physical areas affected are the pineal gland (sometimes called the seat of the soul) and the eyes. It is the gift of Sight both inner and outer.

Also called the Mind Chakra, this links us to our mental body, our light intelligence and psychological characteristics. It stimulates lessons that lead us to our personal wisdom. We all carry intelligence in our cells that reaches beyond knowledge into wisdom. In the words of artist and poet, Brian Andreas, "In my dreams the Angel shrugged and said, 'If we fail this time it will be a failure of imagination,' and then she placed the world gently in the palm of my hand."

Remembering our Divine Wisdom and holding that image in our conscious mind is to increase the possibility that it will

that it will materialize. Encoded in of this chakra is the desire to seek only TRUTH, the uth of your power. The truth of your beauty, your light and y. And because you are seeking truth, you enjoy all the benets of more power, more beauty, more light and more joy each nd every day.

So gently breathe, open, watch, and listen. Place your awareness in the center of your forehead, the third eye chakra and wisdom's radiance to inform and inspire.

6th Chakra Tone: EEE

Affirmation for the Third Eye Chakra:

I easily release my old way of seeing things and allow the truth of my radiance to manifest in every area of my life . . . I allow my imagination to joyously open to happiness and health . . . I walk in well-being . . . I am free from doubt and trust my inner guidance, more and more . . . I am the light I seek.

7th Chakra – The Crown Chakra

Placement – the crown of the head
Color – violet
Tone – MMM - place the sound at top of spinal column, inside the head, drop chin gently toward chest to extend spine; keep sound forward in face, a thin refined sound, very high falsetto.
Area of Impact – pituitary gland, limbic center of brain

This chakra is the entry point for the human life force, which pours endlessly into the human energy system. We could say the element for this chakra is thought—the infinite body of information that informs all chakras. It influences the master gland of the endocrine system, the pineal gland and the higher brain or cerebral cortex. Our brains are limitless. This is our conscious link to source energy—the limitless point of creation, our higher consciousness. This high-pitched tone acts as a doorway opening to the spiritual presence within. The tone of "MMM" or "NNN" is a refined quiet tone stimulating the pituitary gland and opening the crown center. This is best summed up in a prayer by The People of the Hopi nation, "May the door at the top of your head open to the Great Spirit."

Crown Chakra Meditation Exercise
I AM AWARE

Allow yourself to review the places you have gone . . .

Remembering the breath and body that connects you to Earth, the flow of movement and power . . . the song of love in your heart . . . the sound of your soul's song . . . the memories imprinted in your mind . . .

Who is it that remembers? The answer to this is the key itself.

All wisdom is within you . . . nothing is beyond you. It is in your mind, which is but one mind in an ocean of many—connected, contained, intelligent, divine. It is the endless unfolding of potential . . . fully alive . . . ever expanding, always knowing. You consciously hold it in your thoughts.

You are the thoughts that make the pattern. And you are the pattern that makes the thoughts. Breathe in slowly . . . and out . . . in . . . and out. Place your awareness at the top of your head, the crown chakra and let the door at the top of your head open to the Oneness of all.

You are awake; you are aware.

7th Chakra Tone - MMM

Affirmations for the Crown Chakra:

I rest in the beauty of the Divine and am aware of my capacity for creating beauty around me; therefore, I create a beautiful, bountiful life for myself. The healing power of love moves in and through me as I move along the path of life. Inspiration is the expression of my true spirit . . . I let go.

You have actively awakened a formula for profound wholeness. Your voice resonates in the four directions and the Universe hears you. Your heart is open, your body is tuned, and

Keep your thoughts positive because they become your words.
Keep your words positive because they become your behaviors.
Keep your behaviors positive because they become your habits.
Keep your habits positive because they become your values.
Keep your values positive because they become your destiny.

Mahatma Gandhi

7

THE 1 - 2 - 3'S OF SUCCESS

"Give me the "down and dirty" of transformation," she insisted. *"How do I get out of this place? I'M SO SICK OF IT!"*

Frustrated, dangling from the end of her patience and all her positive thoughts, she saw no results. My friend wanted change for herself, and she wanted it *now*. Here was her choice point. She created the most powerful moment for manifesting real change. Energy was summoned. She was focused and deliberate.

With this one goal in mind, to shift the conditions of her moment, we set out together through the landscape of transformation knowing the answer was about to appear. That's how strong her desire was. She spelled out on the table with her finger, "How do I get from here to hear without going there?" We laughed; this was starting to look interesting. We looked at *want* as the distortion of her truth; we then took a bite out of avoidance vs. expansion, resistance vs. freedom. All of this was stirring our creative juices. Sparked by desire, she let out a big

money and the judgments of how her financial life ought to look. Her beliefs about money (e.g., ability to earn it, save it, spend it) were all tied up in the fear that she was inadequate on all fronts. So the authentic truth of her desire was to move out of fear into the domain of NOW where creation occurs.

When we stand in NOW, there is no *past, no future,* and *no present.* There is only BEING in this moment. Changing her focus from *wanting* to be financially secure (*want* = a belief in not having) to already BEING financially secure (an activity taking place in the imagination) revealed her dominant desire, EASE. Once she became conscious of her true intent, ease began downloading a new energy message throughout her body/brain.

Step 2. Feel the sensations of Being at Ease. Simply notice how good it feels to have all your creature needs met. Relax your jaw, let effort and outcomes melt off your body! There is no need to over work this "manifesting" muscle by massaging the image over and over. It is not an intellectual process. Imagination has locked it into place. Just let go and enjoy the moment.

Step 3. Open your mouth and sound Ahhhh. That's correct. This one simple sound activates the source of creation in us all. Keep it simple. Feel the ease! Make the sound! Without needing to make it count or make it "right", just allow yourself to make the sound with an open mind. As you do this, the old program of fear is replaced with new pathways that allow you to be at ease, in the moment!

Sound shifts your world from one of *wishful* to one of *wonderful.* By releasing fear or the desire to change the fear, we allow the limitless possibilities to reveal themselves. It exists already. We just have not been able or willing to see, until we stopped trying to see. Let sound, your sound, do the heavy lifting. Let it clear away the fog of perception and reveal the truth.

Once you stand in ease, you will stay in ease, happily watching your heart's desires flow to you, uninterrupted. *Ease* will be your constant reality, unless you change your attention back to fear. What I appreciate about this Sound*Shifting*® process is how quickly the patterns of pain can be energetically overridden, again and again. So when issues come up, let sound be your default response.

If you follow your bliss, doors will open for you that wouldn't have opened for anyone else.

Joseph Campbell

Because it's impossible to completely eradicate old systems, take heart in knowing that you will either activate them less or be amused by them when they surface in your life. Just remember, you can choose to shift these frequencies of belief at any time and anywhere.

Welcome to the land of magic and miracles. *You* are the miracle. Sound seals the deal on your desire. And as you continue making this open sound, feel it light up every molecule in your body.

That's right, *imagine it!* Watch as the picture inside your imagination gets stronger. Ease now drapes over your shoulders like a rich velvet cape studded with precious jewels, glistening with the shimmering facts and facets of YOU. You are safe, secure and valued.

This feeling sensation is the Universe's way of saying, "Congratulations! You hit this one out of the park! You nailed it! You are the cat's meow and THE only reason I exist."

Sing your heart out!

Reading Room

Beaulieu, John. *Music and Sound in the Healing Arts* (Station Hill, 1987).

Brewer, Chris & Don Campbell. *Rhythms of Learning* (Zephyr, 1991).

Campbell, Don. *The Mozart Effect* (Avon Books, 1997).

Doidge, Norman, M.D. The Brain That Changes Itself (Penguin Books, 2007).

Gaynor, Mitchell L., M.D. *The Healing Power of Sound: Recovery from Life-Threatening Illness Using Sound, Voice, and Music* (Shambala, 2002).

Goldman, Jonathan. *Healing Sounds* (Element, 1992).

Gunther, Bernard. *Energy, Ecstasy and Your Seven Vital Chakras* (Newcastle, 1983).

Halpern, Steven. *Tuning the Human Instrument* (Spectrum, 1980).

Judith, Anodea, Ph.D. *Eastern Body/Western Mind: Psychology and the Chakra System as a Path to the Self* (Celestial Arts 2004, revised).

Keyes, Laurel Elizabeth. *Toning: The Creative Power of the Voice* (DeVorss, 1973).

the Human Voice (Musikarma Publishing, 2005).

Pert, Candace, Ph.D. *Molecules of Emotion: The Science Behind Mind-Body Medicine* (Scribner, 1997).

Tomatis, Alfred A. *The Conscious Ear* (Station Hill Press, 1991).

About The Author

Tryshe Dhevney

In May of 2000, Tryshe was told by doctors that there was no longer anything they could do to treat her hepatitis C and liver disease; she was advised to "get her affairs in order." Five months later, doctors were mystified when tests revealed that she was disease-free and virus-free. Tryshe had healed herself through the power of toning, what she now calls SOUND*Shifting*®.

Today, Tryshe leads workshops nationwide designed to support others to generate their own healing tones that allow optimum health and well being. She lives in Tucson, Arizona, where she recently celebrated her ten-year anniversary of complete freedom from liver disease and any active hepatitis C virus. Her doctor now claims she is "cured."

Along with SOUND*Shifting*®, Tryshe also created the highly acclaimed and nationally recognized Life Scripting Process where she combines traditional theater, recovery therapy, and spiritual disciplines to create living art for social change. Her innovative approach to prevention and education around addiction and young people has brought her to [illegible]

[illegible] tures nationally and internationally. Her work with sound, movement, and authentic expression has been acknowledged as ground breaking. She shares her unique body/voice integration and sound-healing work at Canyon Ranch Health Resort and on Queen Mary 2 Transatlantic Crossings, at Miraval Life In Balance, AZ; Onsite Experiential Workshops, TN; Red Mountain Resort, UT; Sierra Tucson, AZ; Sunstone Cancer Support Foundation, AZ; and Rutgers University, NJ.

Her accomplishments and honors include:

- *Founding Director, Coming To, Tucson, AZ*
- *Founder/Artistic Director, Teens Kick Off, San Francisco, CA*
- *Artist in Residence, Ensemble Theatre Company, Mill Valley, CA*
- *Founder/Artistic Director, Coming 2, Seattle, WA*
- *Recipient of the Outstanding Performance Award, John F. Kennedy Center for the Performing Arts*
- *Recipient of the KOMO TV and PEMCO Financial Centers HOMETOWN HERO Award for Making our community a safer place to live*
- *Former member of the Obie Award-winning Theatre Workshop Boston, OM Theatre Company*

Other Products by Tryshe Dhevney

Chakra Tones Home Audio Course

Tryshe Dhevney's CD, Chakra Tones Home Audio Course, offers a practical guide to the primordial tones that research has shown impact the molecular structure of matter. Use these tones to shift into optimal health and emotional well-being.

LAPIS ENSEMBLE CD

"As I relax into the richly textured music of LAPIS ENSEMBLE, I experience vibrational healing at its most fundamental. Tryshe Dhevney and Chandra Lear have created music that is a restorative journey for the body, mind and spirit...one of sonic immersion that inspires, expands and sustains well-being."

— Andrew Weil, M.D., Best selling author and integrative-medicine pioneer

Chakra Sound Meditation

Printed in the United States of America by Lightning Source

LaVergne, TN USA
15 February 2010
173104LV00001B/2/P
9 780979 715914